THE MAGIC OF
COOLE

John Feehan and *Grace O'Donovan*

OPW

Oifig na nOibreacha Poiblí
The Office of Public Works

THE MAGIC OF COOLE

Baile Átha Cliath
arna fhoilsiú ag Oifig an tSoláthair.

Le ceannach díreach ón
Oifig Dhíolta Foilseachán Rialtais, Teach Sun Alliance,
Sráid Theach Laighean, Baile Átha Cliath 2,
nó trí aon díoltóir leabhar.

Dublin.
Published by the Stationery Office.

To be purchased through any bookseller,
or directly from the
Government Publications Sales Office,
Sun Alliance House,
Molesworth Street, Dublin 2.

Printed in the Republic of Ireland by Betaprint Ltd.

Design by Luly Mason, Éigse Ltd.

ISBN 0-7076-0295-5

ACKNOWLEDGEMENTS

We would both like to acknowledge the
inspiration and guidance of the many
mentors who have down the years kindled
our love of the limestone country of South
East Galway and Clare, and our own
partners and families.

John Feehan and Grace O'Donovan

Photographic acknowledgements :

John Feehan: pages 16, 17, 35, 36, 39, 40, 41, 51,
53, 55.
Jonathan Mason and Paul Mills, Éigse Ltd.:
pages 9, 11, 12, 13, 23, 25,   31, 34, 38, 41,
45, 50, 54, 61.
Michael O'Dwyer: Cover and pages 17, 19.
Bord Fáilte: page 63.
Paddy O'Sullivan: page 42.
ERA-MAPTEC: pages 14, 15.
Richard Mills: page 19.
Terry Dunne: page 28.
Colin Smythe Publishers: pages 64, 65, 66, 67,
68, 69.
National Library of Ireland: page 59.

CONTENTS

INTRODUCTION

The natural world provides much of the inspiration for art, poetry and music. Every landscape has the power to inspire, but some have a special magic. Coole is one such place.

For William Butler Yeats, Ireland's best-known poet, there was another dimension to landscape, one through which other, richer worlds were glimpsed. In the wilderness of the woods at Coole he found the entrance to another world, which he struggled through his poems to find the words to express. The natural world at Coole has inspired some of the finest poetry in English: and not just the poems Yeats wrote specifically about Coole itself, for its magic infused all of his poetry during his most creative years.

But Yeats's hostess, Lady Gregory, was the real heart of Coole. She was one of the most important figures in the Irish Literary Renaissance of the early 20th century, not only because of her own considerable achievement as a playwright, but also because of the way she transformed Coole into a focal point for those who shaped that movement, making it a place they would return to time and again to talk, to plan, to derive inspiration.

But the woods and lakes at Coole were richer even than Yeats divined. The Seven Woods which so enchanted Lady Gregory and her guests held whispers of a more ancient ancestry, of which the literary visitors were scarcely aware: remnants of the earlier natural forest cover, and the disappearing lake and river – which so disconcerted the young Augusta when she first came to live at Coole as William Gregory's young bride – are part of the finest turlough complex not merely in Ireland but in all the world.

The Gregorys first came to Coole in the 1770s; Robert Gregory (1727–1810) shaped his new demesne around the woods and the lake, creating a world where the man-made blended into the natural in a new way, a way which somehow managed to trap the mystery and the wonder of the natural world. The natural world wove itself round the house and the demesne – although perhaps the intention was to do the opposite.

Lady Gregory died on 22 May 1932. In one sense, the magic of Coole has been in abeyance since the demolition of the Great House in 1941, a time when more immediate concerns occupied the minds of most people. Coole Garryland is now a National Nature Reserve managed by the National Parks and Wildlife Service of the Office of Public Works, whose aim is to preserve its rich natural and cultural heritage. The restoration of the outbuildings to house the new Interpretative Centre, and the long-term programme now under way to restore the woods and turloughs as far as possible to their original character, mark the beginning of a new era. The magic of Coole is still there, waiting to be rediscovered.

I walked among the seven woods of Coole:
Shan-walla, where a willow-bordered pond
Gathers the wild duck from the winter dawn;
Shady Kyle-dortha; sunnier Kyle-na-no,
Where many hundred squirrels are as happy
As though they had been hidden by green
boughs
Where old age cannot find them; Pairc-na-lee,
Where hazel and ash and privet blind the paths;
Dim Pairc-na-carraig, where the wild bees fling
Their sudden fragrances on the green air;
Dim Pairc-na-tarav, where enchanted eyes
Have seen immortal, mild, proud shadows
walk;
Dim Inchy wood, that hides badger and fox
And marten-cat, and borders that old wood
Wise Biddy Early called the wicked wood:
Seven odours, seven murmurs, seven woods.
I had not eyes like those enchanted eyes,
Yet dreamed that beings happier than men
Moved round me in the shadows, and at night
My dreams were cloven by voices and by fires;
And the images I have woven in this story
Of Forgael and Dectora and the empty waters
Moved round me in the voices and the fires,
And more I may not write of, for they that
cleave
The waters of sleep can make a chattering
tongue
Heavy like stone, their wisdom being half
silence.
How shall I name you, immortal, mild, proud
shadows?

I only know that all we know comes from you,
And that you come from Eden on flying feet.
Is Eden far away, or do you hide
From human thought, as hares and mice and
coneys
That run before the reaping-hook and lie
In the last ridge of the barley? Do our woods
And winds and ponds cover more quiet woods,
More shining winds, more star-glimmering
ponds?
Is Eden out of time and out of space?
And do you gather about us when pale light
Shining on water and fallen among leaves,
And winds blowing from flowers, and whirr of
feathers
And the green quiet, have uplifted the heart?

I have made this poem for you, that men may
read it
Before they read of Forgael and Dectora,
As men in the old times, before the harps
began,
Poured out wine for the high invisible ones.

September, 1900

W. B. Yeats, Prefatory poem to
The Shadowy Waters, 1906

THE WATERS OF COOLE

Our own river that we catch a glimpse
of now and again through hazel
and ash, or outshining the silver beech
stems of Kyle Dortha,
has ever been an idler.
Its transit is, as has been said of human
life, 'from a mystery through a mystery
to a mystery'.

Lady Gregory, *Coole,* 1931

A few miles from the town of Gort in east Galway is Coole Lough, a small and lovely lake which occupies the bottom of a shallow depression in the wooded limestone. But this is not just a beautiful place. It is an amazing and fascinating place, because Coole River is not simply another river: it is a river which appears out of nowhere and empties itself into what might look like a bottomless lake – a lake with no outflow.

VANISHING LAKES

At sudden thunder of the mounting swan
I turned about and looked
where branches break
The glittering reaches of the flooded lake.

W.B. Yeats, 'Coole Park and Ballylee, 1931'

Coole Lough is an exceptionally fine example of a turlough – a word which comes from the Irish words *tuar loch*, meaning a dry lake, which is appropriate, because these features are unique to Ireland. Turloughs are among the most distinctive landscape features to be found in the lowland limestone country of East Galway and East Clare. For much of the winter the turlough is an open expanse of water, often teeming with wildfowl, and visitors at this time may be confused when

these often quite large lakes are not to be found on the map! The only clue to their peculiarity is the way that stone field walls plunge heedlessly into the water. In summer, the lake is gone, reduced to a small pond (if it has survived at all) and surrounded by open grassland where sheep and cattle graze.

There are two other turloughs in the vicinity of Coole. Garryland Turlough is to the west of Coole, and Newtown Turlough is situated to the south, just outside the Reserve. All of these are classed among the best examples of their kind, and are of international importance.

Coole Turlough

How Turloughs are Formed

After the last Ice Age about 10,000 years ago, many of today's turloughs were just ordinary lakes occupying ice-hollowed basins in the limestone. We know this by looking at the sediments to be found at the bottom of turloughs, which are typical lake sediments laid down in the period immediately following the Ice Age. These sediments lie directly over drift material or till, deposited on the surface by the retreating ice. The lakes were formed over limestone bedrock which is very permeable and easily dissolved away by rainwater, which is slightly acid. Over a long period of time the acid rainfall has eaten away much of the limestone. Very little water flows as streams on the surface in this area; instead the streams flow underground, in caverns in the limestone.

Because the limestone underneath has been so honeycombed by weathering and erosion, the lakes at the surface are often leaky. Instead of streams flowing in and out of these lakes in the normal way, water wells up through springs from below as the water table rises, and likewise disappears through swallow holes in the limestone when the water table drops. Indeed, the diurnal movement of the water table where it is connected to the tidal action of the sea can be observed as far as five kilometres inland in some turloughs when they are not flooded.

In postglacial times, an aureole of fen peat formed around the lake margins which in turn were surrounded by natural woodland. As the lakes gradually became turloughs, the exposed soils began to support herbaceous vegetation in summer.

Garryland

Buckthorn

The uniqueness of the turloughs results from the combination of several special features. The high water table means that there are extensive wetlands surrounding the turloughs. Since the limestones are very pure, the weathering process releases very little in the way of plant nutrients – most critically there is little available phosphorus, and what little there is is easily leached out of the wet soils.

In consequence, the wetlands are high in lime but low in plant nutrients. In the language of the ecologist, they are *oligotrophic calcareous grasslands*, only capable of supporting low intensity farming. However, the annual winter overflowing of the turloughs bring an influx of nutrients to the fringing grasslands every year. Lime ($CaCO_3$) dissolved in the water carried in during winter tend to form a white coating on the vegetation when the waters retreat.

In earlier times particularly, these areas of open grassland fertilised by this annual application of free fertiliser provided excellent summer grazing, and the herbaceous sward was of great importance in the local farming economy. In more recent times, many of these wetlands have been drained to extend the grazing season, and with the availability of artificial fertilisers the unique natural application of fertiliser by flooding has declined in significance. However, drainage and the application of artificial fertiliser totally destroys their unique natural character. Because the soils are often thin, they cannot withstand the prolonged grazing period without becoming severely damaged, and the distinctive vegetation caused by the fluctuations of the water table disappears. As a result, there are now as few as sixty turloughs of any reasonable size (i.e. greater than 10 hectares) left.

The regular annual fluctuation in the water table keeps trees and shrubs back from the edge of the turloughs, but a vanguard of hawthorn, blackthorn and buckthorn stands at the line of the winter floods ready to march forward should a permanent fall in the water table permit it. However, there is also some evidence that trees would extend much further down some turloughs but for grazing.

The following two satellite images show the difference between summer and winter water levels at Coole turlough. They are false colour images with grassland showing up as bright green, water as dark blue and bare soil and rock as pink.

The first image, taken in the winter when the water table is at its highest, shows a large expanse of dark blue over the central area. This is the full extent of the turlough.
The patchwork of agricultural fields surrounding the turlough forms a mosaic of pinks and greens. The bright pink area to the left is the bare limestone of the edge of the Burren.

Satellite image – winter level

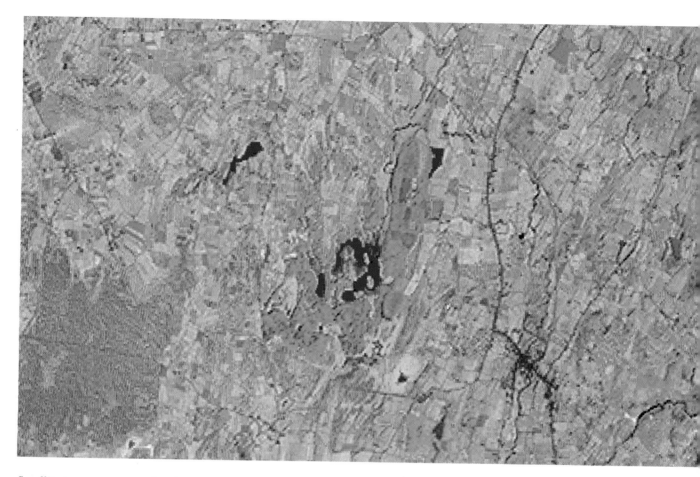

Satellite image – summer level

The second image, at the same scale, shows the turlough in summer when the water level has dropped considerably. The water is now reduced to a small area in the centre of the picture. The predominantly dry turlough now shows up as bright green indicating that it is good grazing pasture.

THE VEGETATION
OF THE COOLE TURLOUGHS

The turloughs of Coole and its surrounding area experience the greatest changes in water level of all the turloughs: up to nine metres in places. Also, in the summer, when the water has disappeared, periods of drought are not unusual because the limestone is so free-draining. Thus, any plants which colonise this landform have at least three major problems to contend with: a very great fluctuation in water level, possible drought, and heavy grazing in the summer months. This is indeed reflected in the vegetation, and depending on the rate of filling and the length of time that the water stays in the turloughs, zones of different plant communities are formed up its sides. As a result, the vegetation of the turloughs forms a unique collection of species.

Starting from the bottom, where water is permanently present, many truly aquatic plants are to be found such as the pondweeds (*Elodea, Potamogeton*), water starwort (*Callitriche*) and water milfoil (*Myriophyllum*). In the shallow water near the edge, floating sweet grass, floating foxtail, shoreweed, fool's watercress and amphibious bistort are often abundant. Around the water's edge, where boulders generally occur, a distinctive moss called willow moss (*Fontinalis antipyretica*) is found. As the Latin name *antipyretica* suggests, this was used as packing material in walls to prevent the spread of fire. It prefers slowl-moving lake or stream water as a rule but it is also a characteristic feature of turloughs.

Other semi-aquatic species are found also, such as water mint, horsetails, water butter-cup and watercress.

Silverweed

Moving up the turlough sides other herbaceous species become dominant. These areas are regularly flooded and a sedge/rush community is common – slender spike rush (*Eleocharis*) and black sedge (*Carex nigra*) in particular.

Carnation sedge and autumnal hawkbit are very characteristic of the zone below the tree zone.

Moving further up from the bottom of the turlough, there may be carpets of silverweed (*Potentilla anserina*) and fiorin, along with the very rare fen violet (*Viola persicifolia*).

In these islands, this violet is found only in fens in eastern Britain (where it is becoming increasingly rare), and this western outpost where it is locally abundant. Plants in the sward here may also have to survive periods of drought in summer.

Fen violet Viola persicifolia

Cinclidotus fontinaloides

The upper reaches of the turlough are less affected by the water table and may be flooded only occasionally. Here we find species which are moderately tolerant of flooding, such as buckthorn and a tall herb community which includes meadowsweet (*Filipendula ulmaria*). There are other tree or shrub species present here such as hawthorn, blackthorn, ash, guelder rose and spindle. Holly is extremely sensitive to flooding, and dead saplings or trees around turloughs give a good indication of the height of flooding attained in winter. Above this level, if the area surrounding the turlough is undisturbed, the dominant vegetation will be oakwood or limestone heath. Garryland Turlough and its surrounds are probably the best examples of how the natural vegetation would have developed in the past.

Often rimming the edges of turloughs on damp rocky slopes above the line of flooding is one of the special plants of the Burren: shrubby cinquefoil (*Potentilla fruticosa*).

This shrub is very rare in these islands in the wild, found only in isolated places in the north of England and here in the Burren. Its more usual home is in the Alps and southeast Sweden, and it is a splendid sight when it flowers in June and July. Another remarkable species indicative of turloughs is a black moss called *Cinclidotus fontinaloides*. This normally inconspicuous moss is a very good guide to the level that water has reached in the turlough throughout the year. It is almost ubiquitous from the bottom of the turlough to the top, and may be found a considerable way up tree trunks around the rim of turloughs marking the uppermost limits of flooding.

A notable feature of turloughs in the summer, when the water level has dropped, is layers of what looks like papery material on the surface of the vegetation. This is composed of algae left stranded by the retreating water, which have dried out to form a papery mat over the bottom of the turlough.

17

ANIMAL LIFE IN THE TURLOUGHS

Turloughs are a difficult habitat for dry land animals, and especially for small animals which cannot flee rapidly-rising flood waters. The alternation between dry and flooded conditions makes it difficult for small animals to survive – unless they can complete their life cycle in a few months. But where conditions in parts of the turlough approximate those of rivers and streams – as is often the case, most forms of aquatic life thrive (frogs, newts, sticklebacks, snails, fishes, insects etc.).

But the species which can meet the harsh conditions imposed by turlough life often occur in prodigious numbers, especially small crustaceans like water fleas which thrive in the productive waters of the turlough, which are nourished by a regular annual inflow of nutrients from animal dung.

The crustacean par excellence of the turloughs is a fascinating little creature: the freshwater fairy shrimp (*Tanymastix*) whose life cycle is beautifully adapted to turlough life and which in Ireland occurs nowhere else.
Tanymastix spends the summer as drought-resistant eggs in the soil on the turlough floor; when the turlough floods, the eggs hatch immediately, and in two months the young attain adult status, and reproduce before the retreat of the flood brings their short life to an end. Large numbers of eggs are produced which will only hatch when they have endured a period of desiccation.

A distinctive invertebrate fauna haunts the water's edge, dominated by carnivorous ground beetles, wolf spiders and centipedes. These creatures hibernate above flood level, and in spring and summer they hunt the receding shore line in search of dead or stranded aquatic animals such as caddis worms. Some are turlough specialists, seldom found anywhere else; they include the ground beetles *Badister meridionalis* and *Agonum livens*.

Turloughs which have lakes and ponds are colonised each year by a range of summer migrants – especially those which can fly into this small world of annual opportunity and make a good living before times become hard and they take to the wing again with their offspring.

Whooper swans

BIRD LIFE ON THE TURLOUGH

The most striking animals of the larger turloughs (including Coole) are the birds which arrive in winter. The most famous of all the birds here of course are the swans, immortalised in Yeats's famous poem:

The trees are in their autumn beauty,
The woodland paths are dry,
Under the October twilight the water
Mirrors a still sky;
Upon the brimming water among the stones
Are nine-and-fifty swans.

The nineteenth autumn has come upon me
Since I first made my count;
I saw, before I had well finished,
All suddenly mount
And scatter wheeling in great broken rings
Upon their clamorous wings.

I have looked upon those brilliant creatures,
And now my heart is sore.
All's changed since I, hearing at twilight,
The first time on this shore,
The bell-beat of their wings above my head,
Trod with a lighter tread.

Unwearied still, lover by lover,
They paddle in the cold
Companionable streams or climb the air;
Their hearts have not grown old;
Passion or conquest, wander where they will,
Attend upon them still.
But now they drift on the still water,
Mysterious, beautiful;
Among what rushes will they build,
By what lake's edge or pool
Delight men's eyes when I awake some day
To find they have flown away?

W.B. Yeats: 'The Wild Swans at Coole'

Three species of swans gather at Coole in the winter: Bewick's swan, whooper swan and mute swan. Other birds which occur in large numbers in winter include widgeon, teal and mallard – though much fewer take up residence here than in such larger turloughs as Rahasane. Shoveller, pintail, tufted duck, golden plover, redshank and curlew are also present in smaller numbers. Rahasane is an internationally important wetland where many thousands of ducks – widgeon, teal, mallard, pintail, shoveller and all three species of swans gather. The turloughs are probably responsible for the occurrence far from the sea of the ringed plover, a shore wader which breeds here on the limestone pavements many miles from the sea.

RIVERS
IN THE UNDERWORLD

The River Coole has its source in a larger lake, Lough Coutra, on the other side of Gort. The stream which flows into Lough Coutra rises at the north-west end of Slieve Aughty as the Owendalullegh River. Water flows out of the north end of Lough Coutra as the River Beagh, and after following a meandering course westwards for three kilometres or so this river is suddenly and dramatically swallowed by the limestone in a wide and cavernous depression known as the Devil's Punchbowl.

The next time the river appears (briefly) above ground is in a hollow called Blackweir or Blackwater, in which the water rises from and sinks into bedding planes in the limestone. It was formerly visible in several other pits and chasms further along , most notably in two vertical pits called the Ladle and the Churn, formed by collapse of the underground limestone roof of the river in its unseen tunnel below. The Churn is like a deep and frightening well three metres across. It gets its name from the noise it made during times of flood, which reminded people of some-body churning. The Ladle is so-called from its shape – the handle being the deep ravine through which it flows into the spoon, where it sinks under a perpendicu-lar rock at the bottom of a steep-sided hollow.

Lady Gregory records some of the folklore attaching to this extraordinary place:

Two men went into a field near to where the river rises one night to catch rabbits. And when they were standing there they heard a churning. So they went on a little way and they heard a tambourine below, music going on and the beating of a drum. So they moved a little further and

Lough Coutra

Devil's Punchbowl

Pollduagh

Doo Lough

then they heard the sound of a fiddle from below. So they came home and caught no rabbits that night.

Lady Gregory, *Coole*, 1931

Half a kilometre further on the river surges once more into the daylight from beneath a natural rock arch at Pollduagh Rising. Pollduagh is an impressive cavern more than six metres wide and nearly two metres high; the dark water fills the cavern from wall to wall as it surges forth.

When it leaves Pollduagh the river has a new name, the Cannahowna. It now flows north-eastwards, through the town of Gort and on as far as the old castle of Kiltartan, four kilometres north of Gort, where it disappears once again at Polltoophill. It now heads across to the west towards Coole, sinking and rising several more times in the old demesne of Coole before finally reaching Coole Lough. On the west bank of the lake the water sinks into a wide bedding cave (which can be explored for 30 metres or more) and flows underground into Doo Lough, which lies a short way to the west, from which it again creeps quietly underground in a pile of boulders at the base of a small cliff at the north end of the lake. From here it seeps through the limestone to Caherglassaun Lough to the north-west, another wonderful area with a cluster of potholes, eventually reaching the sea; at Kinvara the water finally surfaces in off-shore risings.

The Boleyneendorrish River also rises on Slieve Aughty and flows north to sink in two swallow holes west of Ballylee, from where it makes its way through the darkness underground to Coole, just as Yeats imagined. The third major stream which rises on the north slopes of Slieve Aughty, the Owenshree River, also makes its way underground to Coole Lough, so that Coole can be thought of as the centre of an extensive drainage system that includes all three of the major rivers which flow off Slieve Aughty, as well as the rivers, lakes and turloughs in the limestone area to the south-west of Coole.

In the underground stretches where they are hidden from sight, the rivers make their way through passages in the honeycombed limestone. The underground caves and tunnels which are currently active are more or less inaccessible, but the process of limestone erosion underground has been going on for thousands of years, and as the level of the limestone has been progressively lowered, older stream passages have been abandoned as the streams find their way to a lower level.

A good example of such an abandoned stream channel is Coole Cave, which has fine dripstone formations and stalactites.

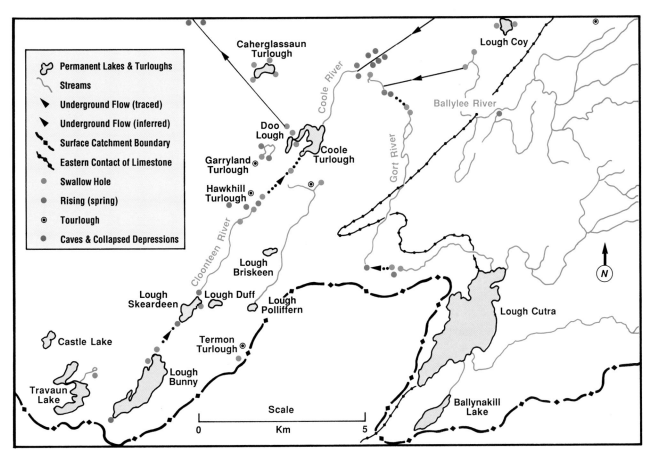

Coole Cave

THE WOODS

"These woods have been well loved, well tended by some who came before me, and my affection has been no less than theirs. The generations of trees have been my care, my comforters. Their companionship has often brought me peace."

Lady Gregory, *Coole*, 1931

THE SEVEN WOODS

*Shan-walla, where a willow-bordered pond
Gathers the wild duck from the winter
dawn;...
Dim Páirc-na-carraig, where the wild bees
fling
Their sudden fragrances on the green air;...
Seven odours, seven murmurs, seven
woods.*

W.B. Yeats,
prefatory poem to *The Shadowy Waters*, 1906

Because of Yeats, the woods at Coole are known by name to people all over the world. Yeats refers several times to the Seven Woods of Coole; in fact there are more than seven. The woods were greatly loved and cared for by the Gregorys, and every grove and plantation had its carefully chosen name. Most were named for some local topographical feature, but some were called after people. There was a copse called the Isabella Wood which was planted by a member of the family in memory of his childless wife, so that her name might live on in these trees. And a corner of the woods planted with larch trees was named after the garden boy who planted them not long before his death, and whose name clung to this corner of the woods thereafter.

But most are simple Irish names which refer to some distinguishing feature: kyle dorcha', the dark wood; kyle-na-no, the nutwood; inchy wood, the wood of the island or water meadow. Several feature the word *páirc*, a field: *páirc-na-lee*, the calves' field; *páirc-na-carraig*, the rocky field; *páirc-na-tarbh*, the field of the bulls. These *páirc* woods were most probably fields when the Gregorys acquired Coole, and were originally planted to woodland by Richard Gregory, the Nabob. The seventh wood, Shan-walla (*sean bhealach*, the old way) took its name from the avenue to the old house, which ran through it. The present avenue runs through open parkland. When it enters the woods it runs between two lines of tall Ilex or holm oak trees, which were much beloved of Lady Gregory. These were planted around 1858 by Lady Gregory's mother-in-law.

Inchy wood ('that wild unplanted wood' as Lady Gregory called it) was regarded as the strangest of the woods, and steeped in folklore:
Some cedars [growing there] were believed to have come from seed dropped by birds that had travelled home from the Holy Land. It lies beyond the rock cavern where the water of the lake disappears from us, on its hidden journey to the sea. The water that had known unearthly visitors, heard unearthly sounds at its rising, is not without them as it vanishes from our sight.

Lady Gregory, *Coole*, 1931

The woods at Coole are not wildwood, areas of natural woodland that show little human interference. They are managed woods, parts of which have their origins in the natural woodland cover which can still be found in odd corners, especially on the far side of the lake, but their natural character has been overlain by forestry practice that extends back for upwards of 200 years. Lady Gregory's husband was a great lover of trees, but not of native trees especially. He had a passion for exotic conifers – coniferomania was a widespread hobby among certain of the landed gentry at the time. Lady Gregory tells us of the 'rare pines that now tower skyward' – and it is such a pity that the value and significance of this collection of rare conifers was not appreciated when the estate was acquired by the Forest Service, for most of these rare exotics have now disappeared. Those which remain are mostly western red cedars and Monterey cypress. A fine avenue of Monterey cypress separates what was formerly the Back Lawn of Coole from the Hobble Field, both of which are now planted with Norway spruce.

All the native tree species will be found in the woods at Coole, side by side with introduced species, of which beech is the most abundant, occurring nearly everywhere. There are some splendid individual trees, both native and introduced, most accessibly near the site of the house and in the vicinity of the car park. These include both species of native oak, holm oak, yew, London plane, horse chestnut and western red cedar. At the lower end of the cypress avenue there is a line of well-grown pink horse chestnuts.

Yew has a special place at Coole, although it is highly poisonous - in Lady Gregory's own words 'dangerous to plant, except among the dead' – which is where it is usually met with. But it is native on the limestone, and beyond the turloughs, at Garryland, there is still some precious yew woodland. The yews at Coole are mostly of the same stock, and here and there in the woods old specimens can be found

Yew

which were apparently deliberately planted in rocky clefts. By the time Yeats came to write his autobiography, Coole had 'lost its great park full of ancient trees'.

The most famous of all the trees at Coole is a copper beech, for this is the species to which the Autograph Tree in the garden belongs . Another famous tree, Lady Gregory's favourite of all the trees at Coole, can still be seen just inside the entrance to the garden. It is now wind-thrown and prostrate, but in its day it would have been a magnificent tree, especially in flower. George Moore records how Yeats and himself sat under it for hours on one occasion arguing about the play *Diarmuid and Grainne* which they were writing, 'Lady Gregory intervening when our talk waxed loud. She would cross the sward and pacify us, and tempt us out of argument.'

Autograph Tree

GARRYLAND

The turlough area is a land of craggy limestone. Over much of it the bare limestone has a very characteristic and attractive flora which includes most of the special plants of the Burren. Only at Garryland does something like a last fragment of ancient woodland still survive. Elsewhere the woodland cover which once dominated the limestone has disappeared, and has been replaced by secondary scrubland.

Although the wood at Garryland has been greatly altered by planting over the centuries, parts of it still retain much of its aboriginal character. The more natural parts of the wood are dominated by oak (*Quercus robur*) and ash, with whitethorn, blackthorn and hazel dominant in more open places. Crab apple (*Malus sylvestris*) is a special feature of the wood, along with holly, wych elm (*Ulmus glabra*), spindle and guelder rose. There is an abundance of juniper, yew and whitebeam (*Sorbus hibernica*) along the fringe of the wood in places, and there are a few areas inside the wood where yew is abundant.

The ground flora includes abundant blue-bell, wood anemone, wood sorrel, enchanter's nightshade, wood avens, bird's eye speedwell, wild arum, self heal and several species of ferns. Among the more special plants are bird's nest orchid (*Neottia nidus-avis*) and dark red helleborine (*Epipactis atrorubens*), a very rare orchid which is more typically associated with the bare open limestone of the High Burren. The bryophyte flora of the woodland floor is spectacularly luxuriant in places where large limestone boulders still cover the ground.

The secondary scrub is still enormously interesting. A good place to see it is on the crags above the south-west corner of Coole Lough, where the vegetation is a prolific and attractive grassland flora, now reverting again to scrub. The patchy grassland

Dunowen

looks wonderfully natural – but if you look carefully you will see a massive stone wall that runs all around the edge of the rock table; this wall is now toppled in most places, but originally it stood several metres high. It is from this feature that the townland on this western side of the lake (Dunowen: Owen's fort) takes its name. It is a most strategic location, because the irregular limestone table on which it stands is surrounded on most sides by vertical cliffs. Lady Gregory seems to have thought that this was the Dún of the legendary King Guaire Aidhne, the famous 6th century King of Connaught whose name is commemorated in the Irish name for Gort (*Gort Innse Guaire*).

Bluebells

Wood anemone

WHAT TO LOOK FOR
WHEN IN THE WOODS

**Broadleaved woodlands, such as those
of Coole and Garryland, go through
many changes throughout the seasons.
These woods not only consist
of many tree species, but include a
rich ground flora of grasses, ferns,
herbs, mosses and fungi.
There is a whole cycle of growth and
decay as the woodland regenerates
itself each year.**

THE WOODS IN AUTUMN

Broad-leaved trees shed their leaves in
preparation for winter. The green chloro-
phyll is broken down and withdrawn into
the stem, and the leaves glow with the reds
and yellows of carotenes and xanthophylls.
An abscission layer develops which will
allow each leaf to fall with the minimum of
disturbance, and a protective layer of cork
is laid down at the base of each leaf to seal
it from infection. These elaborate prepara-
tions are necessary because in the low
temperatures of winter the trees would be
unable to absorb the large amounts of
water from the soil to make up for what
has been lost through the leaves. The
needle-like leaves of conifers are specially
adapted to conserve water, and so they can
be retained through the winter.

Autumn is the time when the fruits on most
of the trees and shrubs ripen. Insect food
is becoming scarce, so the birds and
mammals turn with increasing need to
berries and other fruits; the resident bird
populations are swollen by hordes of
migrants from still colder countries, and
some mammals are beginning to lay in a
store of food for the winter. All of these
are developments which enhance the
opportunities for dispersal.

Woodland plants have evolved all sorts of
ingenious strategies to facilitate the
dispersal of their seeds. Many are
packaged in nutritious carbohydrate-rich
wrappings which are particularly attractive
to birds, enclosed in skins coloured bright
red – the colour birds see best. When the
leaves have been shed, trees and shrubs
whose fruits are dispersed by birds are lit
up for a short time by red berries, but these
quickly disappear, especially when the
winter visitors arrive, and particularly if the
winter is a harsh one when little other food
is available.

Trees which attract birds retain their fruits
on the branches, where the birds can easily
see them. Trees whose fruits are not bird-
dispersed do not produce fruits which are
brightly coloured, and they are generally
shed from the plant when they ripen. Any
help which squirrels or mice or other
animals provide in dispersing the fruits is
incidental; no special attractive colour or
special carbohydrate supplement is
produced. If a squirrel eats an acorn or a
hazel nut, there is no hard seed coat to
protect the seed during its passage through
the animal's digestive system. Most of the
fruits produced by beech and oak fall to
the ground close to the parent, where they
will have little chance of developing
successfully unless a decaying or fallen tree
opens up the prospect of the all-important
light and living space. They may germinate

Rose hip

Rowan berries

Spindles

Crab apple

freely – as beech, ash and sycamore in particular will do – but the seedlings generally wither.

A number of woodland trees and other plants have evolved aerodynamic systems to carry their seeds far from their restrictive parents. Ash, sycamore, lime, maple, birch have wings which help to lift the seeds in the breeze and carry them some distance from the parent – but seldom very far. Feathery parachutes offer the prospect of travel further afield – and this is found in the willows, in wild clematis, as well as numerous herbs.

Crab apple is one of the few trees which is adapted for dispersal by fruit-eating mammals such as ourselves. Other woodland plants use the unintended good offices of passing mammals by hitching a ride. They have developed hooks or bristles which catch in the animals' fur. Wood sanicle, wood avens, water avens and enchanter's nightshade are all common examples which can be seen at Coole.

A profusion of fungi occurs in both the natural and planted woods at Coole, and autumn is the time of year when they are most in evidence. The fungi of woodlands make their living in two main ways: by breaking down the bodies of dead plants (and then using the products to build up their own bodies), or else by attacking and breaking down the bodies of living plants. The great armies of fungi which bring about the decay of dead plants are called saprobes, and those which attack living plants are parasites.

Blusher Amanita rubescens

Codlins and cream Tricholomopsis Rutilans

Nutrient recycling in nature depends on saprobic fungi and bacteria. Without them the whole business of life on earth would grind to a halt. Dead plants would never rot, and the materials which go to make up their tissues would never be recycled in nature – they would simply pile up on the surface. Yet the only time we notice these fungi is when they produce their fruiting bodies, the most conspicuous of which are mushrooms and toadstools. For the rest of the year the main body of the fungus (which consists of a vast network of tiny threads called mycelium) lives below the surface.

But these saprobic fungi are a more important part of the wood than one might think, because many of them have an intimate association with the roots of the forest trees. These special beneficial root-fungus associations are called mycorrhizas, and they are essential to the well-being of the trees, because the fungi assist with the provision of nutrients.

Primroses

THE WOODS IN WINTER

In winter the woods are quiet, echoing now to the new sounds of the noisy birds which inhabit the flooded turloughs. But the woodland still has its community of faithful residents – and certainly for the bird watcher there is always something to see. The tit family is represented by four resident species: great tit (tomtit), blue tit, coal tit and long-tailed tit, but all four can co-exist happily in the woods because each species has its distinct ecological niche, so that there is no direct competition between them.

THE WOODS IN SPRING

Before winter comes, the herbs of the woodland floor withdraw their food reserves and store them in below-ground parts such as stems and roots. At the earliest hint that winter is coming to an end, the leaves of most of the spring-flowering herbs of the woodland begin to peep above ground. They need their early start, because they have to get through as much as possible of the business of the year before the trees come fully into leaf in May, drastically reducing the amount of light reaching the woodland floor. Spring is thus the time of year when the herbaceous plants of the woodland are at their most active, photosynthesising for all they are worth, and carpeting the ground with their blossoms. Parts of the woods are a blue haze in May, when the bluebells flower; elsewhere there are constellations of five-petalled white stars of wood anemones, clumps of incomparable primroses; wood sorrel, beaked parsley, wood avens, wild arum, golden carpets of lesser celandines, shy goldilocks, retiring wood sanicle. The trees themselves flower in spring also, but their flowers are for the most part wind-pollinated, and so they are less conspicuous since they do not need to draw attention to themselves in the way insect-pollinated flowers do. By the middle of summer there will be hardly any sign of these early starters, except for such tell-tale remains as the dried flower-stalks of the bluebells.

The violets at Coole are of particular interest. We have already met the fen violet, which grows on or near the floor of the turlough, and extends only a few feet up the side, where its place is taken by the heath dog violet (*Viola canina*) which grows, sometimes luxuriously if not grazed, in a strip two metres wide. This grades upwards into the territory of the common dog violet (*Viola riviniana*) which ventures a few metres down from the shrub line to meet it.

Safely inside the woodland fringe, the early dog or wood violet (*Viola reichenbachiana*) takes over. The sweet violet (*Viola odorata*) lives in the woods and along hedgebanks away from the turloughs altogether.

Wood violet, which flowers earliest of the four – in April – is identified by its dark purple spur (and a few other details). Common dog violet is not confined to the woods, so it flowers later – it doesn't have to beat the shade in the way wood violet does. It has a stouter, paler-coloured spur. Both are big violets with large rounded leaves. The other two species occur in the open, below the

floodline, so they flower later. Heath dog violet has narrower leaves, smaller flowers and its spur has a yellowish tint. It flowers around the middle of May. When the turlough reaches its summer level, the fen violet flowers. It has tiny pale blue flowers with white spurs, and its leaves are distinctly long and pointed. It is a very rare plant, and becoming increasingly so.

Wild arum
Heath dog violet

Mosses and liverworts are probably at their best at this time of year in the woods. The shade provided by the trees traps moisture essential for their survival and growth in this drought-prone landscape during the summer. Because of the high Atlantic rainfall over the winter months and the variety of surfaces for mosses to colonise, this is one of the richest areas to be found in the country. The luxuriant green mantles and cushions on rocks, and the epiphytic mosses growing on tree trunks and branches, give some parts of these woods an almost tropical appearance in the spring. Spore-bearing capsules, which require lots of moisture for reproduction, proliferate at this time and add further beauty to the scene.

Pine marten

WOODLAND ANIMALS

The woods did not always keep a winter silence, and the frost that hardening the slippery ground gives foxes their safe season in their earths, brings in the woodcocks from the icy bogs and streams, or the frigid terraced limestone of the hills, to snug shelter under hazel boughs and roots and the soft moss that harbours juicy grubs.

Lady Gregory, *Coole*, 1931

Animal life abounds in the woods. The great majority of woodland animals are small creatures, and although they include many of the more special and interesting animals, they are unlikely to catch the eye of the casual visitor.

The more conspicuous animals – the mammals and birds – are generally the ones which caught Lady Gregory's attention and which she describes with such interest in her account of Coole. There is the fox, which she sometimes saw 'at no great distance from the garden gate, pacing slowly, silently, in the centre of one of the green walks', and the badger 'which once crossed Yeats's path so close, so absorbed in its quest, that he touched with his hand its thick covering before it vanished in alarm.' Lady Gregory did not like red squirrels, 'because of their ill treatment of the bark of my young trees', but they are abundant for all that. Rabbits, fieldmice, hedgehogs and stoats are also common. The pine marten, which was seldom seen at Coole in Lady Gregory's time, has now returned, and there is a new arrival in the bank vole, which has only been here for a few years. Most of the common woodland birds can be seen at Coole.

LIFE ON THE LIMESTONE

On the Edge of the Burren:
The Geology of Coole

One particular kind of rock accounts for nearly half of the framework of which the land of Ireland is made: limestone. Where it breaks through the envelope of soil and other materials which usually cover the rock beneath it forms some of the most dramatic landscapes in the country.

There are very few parts of Ireland where limestone so dominates the landscape as in the baronies of Burren in Clare and Kiltartan in Galway. Here the grey limestone attains a thickness of 780 metres, exposed over an area of more than 250 square kilometres.

The story of the limestone begins about 350 million years ago, at the very end of the Devonian period of earth history, when Ireland was still part of the Old Red Sandstone continent. At around this time the sea – which up to this had lain to the south – began to advance northwards over Ireland, ushering in the Lower Carboniferous period of earth history. A thick sequence of lime-rich (carbonate) sediments was deposited in the warm, shallow sea as the millenia passed. This thick blanket of sediment was later compacted and hardened to become limestone rock.

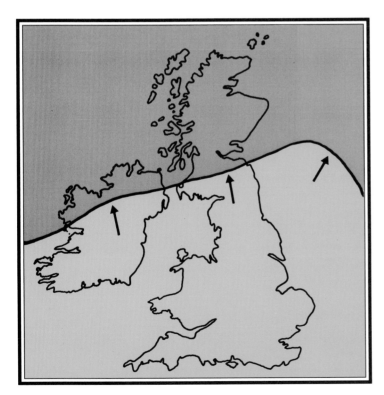

The geography of Britain and Ireland during the lower Carboniferous period.

The Carboniferous Ocean (blue) has advanced slowly northwards, encroauching on the Old Red Sandstone Continent (red), which during the preceding Devonian Period covered the whole of what is now Ireland. The arrows indicate this transgression, as it is called in geological terms.

47

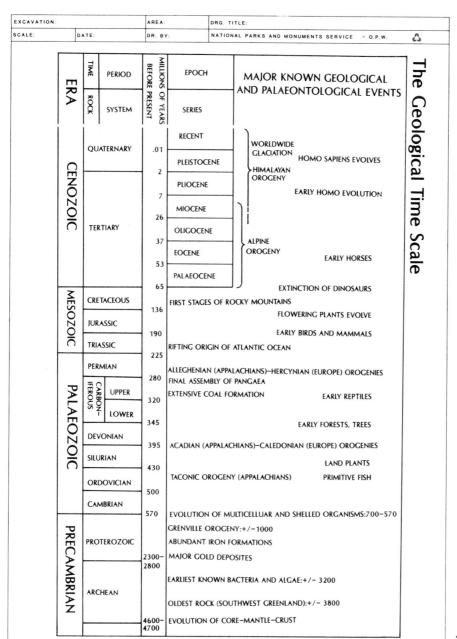

ERA	TIME / ROCK	PERIOD / SYSTEM	MILLIONS OF YEARS BEFORE PRESENT	EPOCH / SERIES	MAJOR KNOWN GEOLOGICAL AND PALAEONTOLOGICAL EVENTS
CENOZOIC		QUATERNARY	.01	RECENT	WORLDWIDE GLACIATION HOMO SAPIENS EVOLVES
			2	PLEISTOCENE	HIMALAYAN OROGENY
		TERTIARY	7	PLIOCENE	EARLY HOMO EVOLUTION
			26	MIOCENE	
			37	OLIGOCENE	ALPINE OROGENY
			53	EOCENE	EARLY HORSES
			65	PALAEOCENE	EXTINCTION OF DINOSAURS
MESOZOIC		CRETACEOUS	136		FIRST STAGES OF ROCKY MOUNTAINS FLOWERING PLANTS EVOLVE
		JURASSIC	190		EARLY BIRDS AND MAMMALS
		TRIASSIC	225		RIFTING ORIGIN OF ATLANTIC OCEAN
PALAEOZOIC		PERMIAN	280		ALLEGHENIAN (APPALACHIANS)–HERCYNIAN (EUROPE) OROGENIES FINAL ASSEMBLY OF PANGAEA
	CARBON-IFEROUS	UPPER	320		EXTENSIVE COAL FORMATION EARLY REPTILES
		LOWER	345		EARLY FORESTS, TREES
		DEVONIAN	395		ACADIAN (APPALACHIANS)–CALEDONIAN (EUROPE) OROGENIES
		SILURIAN	430		LAND PLANTS
		ORDOVICIAN	500		TACONIC OROGENY (APPALACHIANS) PRIMITIVE FISH
		CAMBRIAN	570		EVOLUTION OF MULTICELLUAR AND SHELLED ORGANISMS:700–570
PRECAMBRIAN		PROTEROZOIC			GRENVILLE OROGENY:+/–1000
					ABUNDANT IRON FORMATIONS
			2300–2800		MAJOR GOLD DEPOSITES
		ARCHEAN			EARLIEST KNOWN BACTERIA AND ALGAE:+/– 3200
					OLDEST ROCK (SOUTHWEST GREENLAND):+/– 3800
			4600–4700		EVOLUTION OF CORE–MANTLE–CRUST

The Geological Time Scale

The Geological Time Scale

One of the most characteristic features of the limestone is the way the rock is sculptured into a stepped arrangement of terraces, each terrace separated from the next by a cliff, making the landscape look for all the world like a gigantic stairs. These terraces in the limestone reflect breaks in the cycle of marine sedimentation. Minor terraces often develop along the occasional shale bands which occur in the limestone sequence. The limestone is criss-crossed by sets of joints. These reflect planes of weakness which developed in the rock as a result of squeezing by ancient earth movements. The joints widen as a result of weathering to form grikes. These grikes have their own microclimate, and they harbour a wealth of ferns and other plants.

The 19th century geologist Stackpoole Westropp was only slightly exaggerating when he wrote that 'the joints in the rocks have been so opened up that a man could go down bodily into some of them and disappear from the face of the earth.'

Although there is an abundant fauna of corals and brachiopods in the limestone, fossils are seldom seen clearly on the surface of the rock.
Large productid brachiopods (gigantoproductids) often catch the eye where the stone has been used for building.

Fossils are conspicuous in several places at Coole, including the bare pavement along the western shore of Coole Lough. For the most part the limestone is crinoidal limestone, full of the debris of crinoid or sea-lily skeletons.

Joints

Grikes

*Limestone fossil
at Coole*

Solution of the surface limestone concentrates along the ready-made lines of weakness provided by the grikes. There are three main sets of vertical joints, and they are the main reason why the limestone is so permeable.

Water falling on the surface is simply swallowed up by the open grikes, but down below the surface it continues its work of solution, hollowing out caves and passages in the limestone. In limestone landscapes therefore, water can only flow above ground for a short time before it disappears into the ground to follow a hidden course through the rock, reappearing at the surface somewhere further on. This may happen several times before the streams find their way eventually to the sea, and the Coole River provides a wonderful example.

The special landscape which results from the solution of limestone and underground water circulation is called karst, after the region in Dalmatia and Istria (in what was formerly Yugoslavia) where it is most classically developed.

The Burren is Ireland's finest and most famous karst area, and the Gort-Ardrahan area is often regarded as the best remaining area of relatively intact lowland karst in Western Europe.

WEATHERING OF LIMESTONE

Limestone is composed almost entirely of a single chemical substance, calcium carbonate ($CaCO_3$), which is derived from the skeletons of the animals which lived in the Carboniferous sea. Once the rock comes to the surface it is quickly eaten away by the elements. For limestone the most corrosive agent of erosion is rainwater, because it is a dilute solution of carbonic acid, which simply dissolves the carbonate of which the limestone is composed.

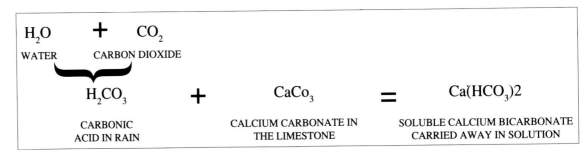

H_2O **+** CO_2
WATER   CARBON DIOXIDE

H_2CO_3 **+** $CaCo_3$ **=** $Ca(HCO_3)2$

CARBONIC ACID IN RAIN   CALCIUM CARBONATE IN THE LIMESTONE   SOLUBLE CALCIUM BICARBONATE CARRIED AWAY IN SOLUTION

THE ICE AGE IN THE BURREN

The gently rounded profile of the Burren today is a legacy of the Ice Age. There is evidence for two late phases of glacier movement across the Burren. During the earlier of these, the ice moved across from Connemara, leaving tell-tale erratics of Galway granite and limestone, notably around the northern slopes of the Burren. Erratics are geological wanderers, boulders carried far from their place of origin by glaciers. During the most recent advance, ice moved over the Burren from the north-east. Occasional glacial striae on the limestone – scratches scored on underlying bedrock by rocks held fast in the grip of the moving ice – also record the direction in which the ice moved, as does the orientation of the swarms of drumlins in the area to the south (especially around Kilfenora). All of these features bear witness to this most dramatic phase of the Burren's recent geological history.

Joints (Aerial view)

THE RETURN OF LIFE AFTER THE ICE AGE

Immediately after the Ice Age, glacial drift (rock debris and clay left behind when the glaciers melted) covered a much larger area of the limestone, especially in low-lying areas. Areas which today are strewn with erratics, such as that east of Mullaghmore, had a deep drift cover. In general we can assume that, in the beginning at least, there was glacial drift wherever there are erratic boulders today.

Once the ice had finally retreated and temperatures rose again, plant life began to return. To begin with the vegetation was

willow-juniper scrub, along with aspen, and such shrubs and herbs as dropwort, crowberry, ferns and various grasses. The spread of downy birch – along with other newcomers such as guelder rose which are characteristic of the open woodland that replaced the earlier vegetation – ended this first phase. The next phase was marked by the arrival and spread of scots pine and hazel, and then later on oak and elm began to spread. The vegetation was still open woodland, with heather and bracken and there was considerable grass cover. This was the landscape into which the first people came in Mesolithic times around 9,000 years ago, fishing and hunting the shores, perhaps penetrating inland to the lakes: today's turloughs were still only lakes in those days.

The story of how the vegetation changed as climate improved is told in the pollen record preserved in the sediments which have accumulated in these lakes since the end of the Ice Age.

Farming in this area began in Neolithic times 6,000 or so years ago, and accelerated with the coming of the Bronze Age 1500 years later. The area had everything the Bronze Age herders required: there was year-round grazing, and there was copper in veins in the limestone.

The great number of wedge graves and earlier monuments testify to the fertility of the soils for early farming peoples, and the assiduity with which they farmed.

As woodland was cleared for grazing and crops the land became increasingly more open, and the characteristic herbs of open ground began to spread. Holly and birch became more important components of the vegetation. The dramatic reduction in farming activity which is the most striking feature of Irish prehistory around 500 B.C. allowed yew, pine and elm to stage a brief recovery on the limestones. Pine seems to have disappeared altogether around 1500 years ago. With the acceleration of farming which occurred in the Early Christian period, tree cover was greatly reduced.

But things were happening at the end of the Bronze Age which the farmers of the time could know little about. The climate became wetter and cooler after 500 B.C.,

exposing the fertile upland fields to the onslaughts of the winds from the Atlantic. Winter gales tore the soil from the limestone and washed even more of the glacial drift into the lakes. The karst – which probably covered only a tiny area after the Ice Age – was initially created by post-glacial erosion, but the area of exposed limestone was increased considerably by human activity. Pockets of glacial drift survive in areas such as Carran and in the Caher valley, and some of the last fragments of old woodland can still be found in such places.

THE FLORA OF THE LIMESTONE

The limestone of western Ireland harbours a spectacular and luxuriant flora. There are some plants here whose true home lies away to the south – species such as the maidenhair fern (*Adiantum capillus-veneris*) and the dense-flowered orchid (*Neotinea maculata*) for example – side by side with others which are more at home in mountains or colder lands to the north: among them spring gentian (*Gentiana verna*), mountain avens (*Dryas octopetala*), bearberry (*Arctostaphylos uva-ursi*), pyramidal bugle (*Ajuga pyramidalis*) and the eyebright (*Euphrasia salisburgensis*). Yet this bewildering assortment consists entirely of plants which are native to Ireland, and not a few have their principal or only stronghold here.

The reasons for this unusual collection of species are not yet clear. It is possible that the range of these species was much greater at some time in the past, but that it has shrunk due to changes in climate, and possibly cultivation, with just a few isolated pockets left. That may explain how these species arrived but it certainly doesn't explain how or why they have survived to the present day. Some unique conditions must exist in the Burren area which are conducive to the survival of both Arctic-Alpine and Mediterranean plants.

Arctic-Alpines normally live in mountainous or cold climates yet they live quite happily in the Burren at sea level, at very equitable temperatures (mean annual temperatures of 10°C) and with very few frosts. In their more usual habitats, they have very severe constraints on their growth for most of the year – for example snow cover, cold temperatures or long periods of darkness. In the Burren none of these constraints apply.

Spring gentian

However, the Burren soils in which these species grow present difficulties to otherwise more competitive species. What are these harsh conditions? Much of the limestone area consists of bare karst with most of the soil cover removed. What little soil remains is held between cracks in the limestone, and as often as not it is very shallow.

The level of available soil nutrients is very low and this, coupled with drying out of these thin soils over the summer months makes it difficult for plants to thrive. Thus, while these Arctic-Alpines are not 'at home' here, they have many problems to contend with, and their particular set of adaptations makes them fit to survive in a landscape that is – from an ecological point of view – as inhospitable as their original home.

The presence of the Mediterranean species is perhaps easier to explain in that the warm oceanic climate is reminiscent of their more southerly home. The drought which they experience in the Burren is also a feature of the Mediterranean climate.

Another factor which adds to the diversity found in the Burren is the variety of soil types which may be present. Drift or till deposited by the ice in the last glaciation is to be found in many parts, and it has a relatively neutral pH (between 5.5 – 6.5). Another soil type, called a rendzina, is derived by direct weathering of the limestone. This is a very black organic soil and has a high pH of 7. In contrast to these neutral or basic soils, some soils are quite peaty, with a pH as low as 4 or 5. This is because some of the drift soils become leached of their nutrients on account of the high rainfall here over the winter months. This can lead to what seems a contradiction in terms: a limestone heath. What is more, these soils can vary over very short distances, juxtaposing heathy plants such as heather with lime-loving plants such as mountain avens *(Dryas octopetala)*, and testing to the utmost the ingenuity of the ecologists who seek to explain these things!

Most of the plants which make up the typical Burren flora can be found on the limestones around Coole, although some, such as mountain avens, are found only on the hills. On the other hand, dropwort *(Filipendula vulgaris)* is seldom found away from the turloughs in the lowland limestone area. For most of this area the dominant natural vegetation cover would be woodland, but this has been lost almost

Spindle

everywhere; the vegetation on most of the craggy limestone today is secondary vegetation which developed after the removal of the natural woodland cover by fire or other forms of human erosion. Buckthorn *(Rhamnus frangula* and *Rhamnus catharticus)*, spindle *(Euonymus europaeus)*, dogwood *(Cornus sanguinea)* and yew *(Taxus baccata)* are conspicuous in this scrub, especially on the woodland fringes.

Juniper *(Juniperus communis)* is dominant over large areas and spectacularly so across the rocks which surround the turloughs to the south and east of Garryland, especially on either side of the causeway that carries the road from Gort to Kinvara.

The flora is at its most splendid in late spring and summer. Bloody cranesbill *(Geranium sanguineum)* is everywhere, its red flowers startling against the grey of the limestone. There are drifts of mossy saxifrage *(Saxifraga hypnoides)* with nodding star-shaped flowers and delicately pink-tipped buds. Several members of the bedstraw family belong to the limestone flora. The most conspicuous, because of its yellow flowers and its smell of new-mown hay, is lady's bedstraw *(Galium verum)* but the others are more characteristic of the limestone. Wild madder *(Rubia peregrina)* is one of the special plants of the Burren. It has four-angled stems with down-turned prickles to assist it in scrambling about the open scrub which it favours, bearing whorls of four to six shiny evergreen leaves which also have hooked edges. It has small greenish-yellow flowers with five petal-like sepals growing in clusters at the base of the leaves. The fruits are pea-sized black berries. Another special limestone bedstraw is squinancywort (*Asperula cynanchica*), which grows out in the open, keeping close to the ground, and produces clusters of small pinkish-white flowers, each with four petal-like corolla lobes. The rarest of the limestone bedstraws is the white-flowered northern bedstraw (*Galium boreale*) which, as its name suggests, has affinities in cooler climes. Another characteristic and rare bedstraw on the limestone is the wood bedstraw (*Galium sterneri*).

The western limestones have two species of eyebright, the common species *Euphrasia officinalis*, and *Euphrasia salisburgensis*, which is especially characteristic of the Burren: it occurs nowhere in Ireland except here and in the Ben Bulben range. It hardly occurs at all in Britain, and on the European mainland it usually keeps to the mountains, though it is not confined to limestone habitats. This is the case with a number of plants which are clearly calcicoles (lime-loving plants) in Ireland. Eyebrights are partial parasites, drawing food from the roots of grasses and other plants.

Yellow centaury (*Blackstonia perfoliata*) adds another colour to the limestone flora. It has large, star-shaped yellow flowers, with pairs of opposite leaves that join to embrace the stem. It is a member of the gentian family (Gentianaceae) but it is another member of the same family that is the unrivalled glory of the western limestones, and of the Burren in particular. The intense blue of the spring gentian (*Gentiana verna*) is indescribable. The flowers are fully an inch across, all the more astonishing because of the dwarf size

Early purple orchid

of the plant, which never gets more than an inch or two off the ground. It grows vegetatively by sending out slender underground shoots from the central rootstock, so that a single plant in a suitable habitat will produce dozens of wide-eyed flowers in patches up to a foot and more across. Another member of the family is the autumn gentian (*Gentianella amarella*) which is widespread in the limestone grasslands, producing its spikes of purple flowers in August and September.

The limestones are a wonderful place for orchids, though many of them are rare and even those which are not are sometimes difficult to find. The commonest species is the early purple orchid (*Orchis maculata*), which is one of the most characteristic and abundant flowers of the early summer. Autumn lady's tresses (*Spiranthes spiralis*) is a small sweet-scented orchid that flowers in the grassland in September. It is inconspicuous, but a great thrill to find. The rarest orchid of the limestone is the spring-flowering dense-flowered orchid (*Neotinea maculata*), a plant whose true homeland is in the area around the Mediterranean.

Other flowering plants which are characteristic of the limestone include bearberry, salad burnet, carline thistle, mountain everlasting and wood sage. The fern which is most especially associated with the pavement is the rare maidenhair fern, which hides deep in the shelter of the grikes.

The species of grass most characteristic of the limestone is blue moor grass (*Sesleria albicans*), which takes its name from the blue sheen on the flowering heads before they open up, and is largely confined to the western limestones.

The limestone also has a characteristic lichen flora. There are many species which will grow only on limestone, and indeed it is possible to use lichens to identify the rock. Among the most characteristic genera are *Caloplaca*, *Aspicilia* and *Verrucaria* .

ANIMAL LIFE

Insect life is diverse and abundant in this species-rich grassland and in the scrub that grows on the limestone. Perhaps the most characteristic and easily recognisable insect is the burnet moth, which has bluish-green forewings with six crimson spots, and crimson hind-wings: warning colours that alert would-be predators of a distasteful or poisonous meal. This enables the moth to fly fearlessly by day, when it is often seen feeding on flowers. The caterpillars (which feed on trefoils and other plants) are yellow with black spots – another warning colour combination.

One of the rarest insects in this habitat is the elusive brown hairstreak, which flies only in sunshine, and so swiftly that it is hard to spot, although it can occasionally be seen feeding on bramble, its favourite flower. It is on the wing mainly in August and September; the caterpillars feed on blackthorn.

Perhaps the most conspicuous insect on the limestone is the brimstone, which is the first butterfly to be seen on the wing when it emerges from hibernation as early as February. It is a wonderful yellow in colour, the sulphur on its wings providing a startling contrast to the purples of knapweed, scabious and clover on which it can be seen feeding in summer. It hibernates under ivy leaves, and when at rest during winter provides one of the most remarkable examples of cryptic camouflage. What makes it especially characteristic of limestone and turlough country is the fact that its caterpillars feed on buckthorn.

LADY GREGORY AND THE MAKING OF COOLE PARK

If you, that have grown old, were the
first dead,
Neither catalpa tree nor scented lime
Should hear my living feet, nor would
I tread
Where we wrought that shall break the
teeth of Time.
Let the new faces play what tricks they
will
In the old rooms; night can outbalance
day,
Our shadows rove the garden gravel
still,
The living seem more shadowy than
they.

W.B. Yeats, 'The New Faces'

THE GREGORYS AT COOLE

The Gregorys had come to Coole in the
1770s, when Robert Gregory (1727-1810),
the great-grandfather of Lady Gregory's
husband, Sir William, returned with his
wealth from India and bought the estate;
in his time he had been an English M.P.
and a director and chairman of the East
India Company. It was essentially he who
created the estate, planting extensively,
and developing a reputation of concern for
his tenants. Arthur Young visited Coole in
1778 and described Robert Gregory's
'noble nursery, for which he is making
plantations'. Robert was succeeded by his
second son, Richard – the eldest son was
disinherited for failing to put an end to his
passion for cock-fighting. Richard had no
children – his most obvious contribution to
today's Coole is the big bust of Macaenas
in the walled garden, which he is said to have
had dragged across Europe by oxcart. He

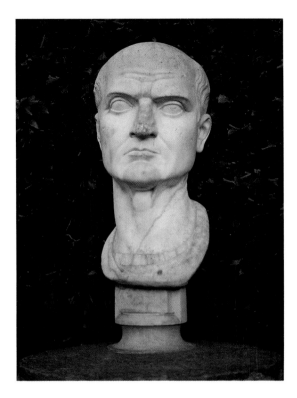

Bust of Macaenas

was succeeded by his younger brother
William, the grandfather of Lady Gregory's
husband, who had been Under-Secretary
for Ireland from 1813 to 1832. He in turn
was succeeded by his son, another Robert
Gregory, who was the first to see Coole as
a home rather than an occasional retreat
from the real world of Dublin and London.
He planted a pinetum – a plantation of
different exotic pines – in the Nut Wood,
scouring the nurseries in England for 'all
the specimens that were invented and got
up by ingenious nurserymen for the
benefit of Coniferomaniacs, as we were
then called'. The Nut Wood became
known as the Rich Wood – the idea being
that only somebody with lots of money
could afford it.

Robert was a good landlord at heart, but a very careless one in the long term. He never raised his tenants' rents because of improvements they had made to their holdings, and they felt such confidence in him that they never bothered with leases. But when in the 1850s he had to sell two-thirds of the estate to pay his racing debts, this easy and careless confidence had disastrous consequences. The new land-owners doubled the rents, ruining most of the tenants and forcing many of them to emigrate. Robert was succeeded by his son William, the future husband of Isabella Augusta Persse.

LADY GREGORY AND COOLE

Isabella Augusta Persse – the future Lady Gregory – was born in 1852 at nearby Roxborough. She has an enduring claim to fame in the history of Irish literature on several counts: because of her part in the founding and early growth of the Abbey Theatre, because of the way Coole Park itself became a place of retreat and inspiration for the Irish Literary Renaissance, and not least because of her own plays. She was also an important collector of folklore, and in her declining years she made strenuous efforts to have the priceless picture collection of her nephew Hugh Lane returned to Ireland. At the age of 27 she married Sir William Gregory, the Master of Coole Park. Augusta did not at first like the dark woods and the disappearing lake at Coole: it was only after the death of Sir William that her interest in the peasant culture all about her began to stir.

*Lady Gregory
on her wedding day*

William Gregory

During the Gaelic Literary Revival in the late 19th and early 20th century Coole became a haven in which the famous sought refuge from time to time, drawn by the hospitality and enthusiasm of Lady Gregory, whom George Bernard Shaw once described as the 'greatest living Irishwoman'.

Here they came together, as the class to which most of them belonged lost its political pre-eminence, to create from the embers of a dying order a new pre-eminence. The names of many of those who contributed to the Literary Revival are engraved on Lady Gregory's Autograph Tree – the copper beech in the walled garden. The first name to be carved on it was that of Yeats himself, whom she asked to cut his initials in the summer of 1898. Here is Lady Gregory's own account of the tree:

And on the great stem, smooth as parchment, of a copper beech whose branches sweep the ground as we come near the gate into the woods, many a friend who stayed there has carved the letters of his name.

W.B.Y. of course, and Jack B.Y. with a graving of the little donkey he loves; and J.M. Synge and AE and An Craoibhin (Douglas Hyde) and John Masefield and Sean O'Casey and as it should be, a very large G.B.S. And this A.J. was cut by Augustus John after his descent from the very topmost boughs where he had left those letters also to astonish the birds of the air.

But alas! once or twice country lads doing some work in the orchard, seeing these

Autograph Tree

signatures, thought it natural to add their own, and these, unknown to literature, may puzzle some future antiquarian.

Lady Gregory, *Coole*, 1931

Others whose initials occur include Katherine Tynan (KHT), Violet Martin (VM: the Ross of Somerville and Ross), Lady Gregory herself (AG) and her son Robert (RG).

*They came like swallows and
like swallows went,
And yet a woman's powerful character
Could keep a swallow to its first intent;
And half a dozen in formation there,
That seemed to whirl upon a
compass-point,
Found certainty upon the dreaming air,
The intellectual sweetness of those lines
That cut through time
or cross it withershins.*

W.B.Yeats, 'Coole Park, 1929'

Many drew inspiration from Coole. Lady Gregory tells us that when Synge visited Coole he never went out on the roads: all his time was spent in the woods. It was these, she says, that were in his mind when he wrote 'Who'll pity Deirdre has lost the twilight in the woods with Naisi, when beech trees were silver and copper and ash trees were fine gold.'

But it was Yeats who drew most from Coole, from the time he first arrived in 1897, in a state of physical and psychological exhaustion from which he was nursed back to health by Lady Gregory. He once described Coole to John Masefield as the most beautiful place in the world. He wrote much of the poetry of his middle period here; five books of his poetry show the all-pervading inspiration of Coole: *In The Seven Woods* (1904), *The Green Helmet and Other Poems* (1910), *Responsibilities* (1914), *The Wild Swans at Coole* (1919) and *The Winding Stair and Other Poems* (1933). Yet, while he stayed in Coole, Yeats really lived in another world. As he wandered the woods and grounds, lost in that landscape of the imagination, he would rarely respond to a greeting from somebody he didn't know, and would only listen 'if you talked of faeries'.

*W. B. Yeats
standing at the top
of the steps in front
of Coole ,
with the front lawn
behind him.*

Like many of his ancestors, William Gregory also had crippling debts; to pay them off he mortgaged Coole to his cousin, paying 4.5% interest on the mortgage. After Sir William's death in 1892, Lady Gregory made the paying off of the mortgage her priority, so that the estate would be free of debt when her only son Robert came of age. But even during those years of financial stringency, Lady Gregory bought and planted trees all the time – especially firs and larches with their 'rosy blossoms and delicate green branches.' She planted thousands of seedlings in the winter of 1885-6 for instance, having saved the money to buy them by going without food in London.

The library

Sean O'Casey said of Lady Gregory that her great loves were books and trees – books nearest her mind, trees nearest her heart. Whenever she received a fee or royalty she would first go out and plant a tree. On the other hand, when a letter arrived in the post which upset her, she would go out into the garden to dig weeds, saying 'so perish all the King's enemies' as she did so. It was Lady Gregory who taught Sean O'Casey to identify trees until he could reel off the names 'the way an eager young man would tell his beads.'

The young wood in front of the house was a lawn in Lady Gregory's day, and here Robert organised cricket matches under the huge Ilex (evergreen oak) which then grew there. Sir William would return from London in early summer just to see the whitethorns in the park in blossom. Lady Gregory herself would stay out late in the woods and grounds because 'one must stand and look at blossoming tree after

tree'. Coole looked especially wonderful in early summer, with an abundance of lilacs and laburnums, and white and pink-flowering horse chestnuts.

The night of the Big Wind in February 1903 brought devastation to Coole, felling many of the great lime trees in the area between the house and the stables as well as the great Ilex on the front lawn (depriving the Coole cricket team of some sort of psychological advantage; having been unbeaten up to this, they now began to lose). Large areas of the woods were flattened, and thousands of spruce and larch trees were lost.

In January 1918 Robert Gregory was killed in Northern Italy during the Great War. It was for his sake that Lady Gregory had worked so hard to keep Coole together, and to free it from its crippling burden of debt. Robert's death knocked the heart out of her life, and she no longer felt the

65

same committment to preserving Coole for the Gregory family. In 1920 most of the estate was sold off under the new Land Acts; lands across the lake were sold to the Congested Districts Board in May, and most of the rest to a group of tenants for £9,000 in November. Lady Gregory retained only the house, garden and some of the woods. On 1 April 1927 she sold what remained to the Ministry of Lands and Agriculture, renting back the house and gardens for £100 a year. She took some consolation from the fact that the Forestry Department would take over after her departure, confident that they would maintain and extend the generations of planting. Her optimism was ill-founded. In 1929 Yeats wrote a famous passage which foretold the future of Coole with depressing accuracy:

Here, traveller, scholar, poet,
take your stand
When all those rooms and
passages are gone,
When nettles wave upon a
shapeless mound
And saplings root among the
broken stone,
And dedicate – eyes bent upon
the ground,
Back turned upon the brightness
of the sun
And all the sensuality of
the shade –
A moment's memory to that
laurelled head.

Coole Park, 1929'

Coole House

Lady Gregory under the Catalpa tree

By the time Yeats came to write 'Coole Park and Ballylee, 1931', Lady Gregory was dying, a tenant on the great estate she once ruled. The poem is filled with Yeats's own nostalgia at the passing of the old order:

We were the last romantics – chose for
theme
Traditional sanctity and loveliness;
Whatever's written in what poets
name
The book of the people; whatever most
can bless
The mind of man or elevate a rhyme;
But all is changed, that high horse
riderless,
Though mounted in that saddle Homer
rode
Where the swan drifts upon a
darkening flood.

Lady Gregory died on 22 May 1932. Nine years later, and despite pleas for its preservation, the house which had played such a notable role in the Literary Renaissance was demolished for building stone. 1941 was a year when these things counted for less than they do today. Having survived the War of Independence – which saw the destruction of so many of the Great Houses – Coole succumbed to the economic war which followed in its wake.

Oliver St John Gogarty described the sad and misguided destruction which followed:

All, all are gone, and the Big House is demolished. Not one of the Seven Woods remains, woods where on a tree you could find the initials G.B.S. or J.M.S.; but the tree may now be on a railway wagon going to supply the demand for building material, though it makes one wonder what can be worth building in a land where there is no reverence for great times and great men.

The Inspiration of Coole:
A Visionary Landscape

Yeats wrote three poems which mention Coole Park by name in their titles.
The earliest is 'The Wild Swans at Coole', the title poem of the volume of poems published in 1919.
The second is 'Coole Park, 1929', the poem which begins with the famous and prescient description of the destruction of the great house quoted above.
The third poem is 'Coole Park and Ballylee, 1931'. But even when Coole is not mentioned by name, you can feel its presence behind many of the poems written by Yeats during this period.

'Coole Park and Ballylee, 1931' was written as a memorial to the fall of the great house which he had come 'to love more than all other houses', and the decline of Lady

W.B. Yeats and Lady Gregory, in front of Coole

Gregory herself, who for 40 years had been 'my strength and my conscience'. It is in the tradition of the English estate poem, or great house poem, in which the poet compliments his patron by praising the prosperity and order of his estate – indeed, it is the last poem in this genre, a tradition which began with Ben Jonson's 'Penhurst'.

There is a comparable but even richer tradition in Irish poetry – and this may have been familiar to Yeats because of his interest in the Gaelic poet Raftery. For Yeats the decline and fall of Coole was symbolic of a more widespread decline: that of the Protestant aristocracy whose order and culture and tradition had been the essential framework of his own turbulent life.
It marks a crisis in Yeats's life; it is one of his most pessimistic poems, and following Lady Gregory's death shortly afterwards he wrote nothing further in verse until 'A Full Moon in March' in 1935.
It is pervaded by images of house, woods and lake, and by a desperate search for human meaning in the symbolism in landscape.

The turlough and the river which feeds it are powerful symbols for Yeats. The stream which flowed under the window of Yeats's tower at Thoor Ballylee disappears underground in a dark pool called Raftery's Cellar, rising again in Coole Park to swell the lake before disappearing again. This stream was for Yeats a symbol of the soul's voyage, whose brief passage through life was followed by death and, after dark purification, reincarnation into this upper world again.

'Coole' *by Robert Gregory*

Under my window-ledge the waters race,
Otters below and moor-hens on the top,
Run for a mile undimmed in Heaven's face
Then darkening through 'dark' Raftery's 'cellar' drop,
Run underground, rise in a rocky place
In Coole demesne, and there to finish up
Spread to a lake and drop into a hole.
What's water but the generated soul?

W. B Yeats 'Coole Park and Ballylee, 1931'

For Yeats, Coole Park was more than the place we see today: indeed, it was more than the place he saw himself. Not just because the house has gone and much else has changed since his time, but because he used the place and other symbols he most loved to express his vision of another world altogether – they were 'epiphanies of a truth beyond the limits of the accident that is Ben Bulben, Coole Park or Lissadell etc.'

In the same way, the paintings of Robert Gregory are visionary landscapes, not the products of the objective curiosity of the scientist. They come out of a tradition in painting which sees the actual world as no more than a shadow of a world of deeper meaning behind.